Veggie Delights

Holistic Health Recipes, Eating Live for Maximum Nutrition and Wellness

2nd edition

K. Akua Gray

BJK Publishing and Distribution
a DBA of Bojakaz Management, LLC
2020

Bojakaz Management, LLC
P O Box 921
Missouri City, Texas 77459
Original Copyright © 2011, 2020 by K. Akua Gray

This publication was designed to provide accurate and authoritative information in regard to the subject matters covered. It is sold with the intention to educate, inform, and empower readers to make their own decisions on health, life, and well-being. If you have concerns about your physical, mental, or spiritual condition consult the appropriate professional.

Cover Design: Cover Fresh Designs
Cover Photos: K. Akua Gray

Printed in the United States of America

ISBN 9780990408925

Also by K. Akua Gray

Naturopathic Reiki I: Opening the Way

☥

Naturopathic Reiki II: The Essentials of Therapy

☥

Naturopathic Reiki III: The Power of the Master

☥

Natural Health and Wellness: The Consultant Manual

☥

Holistic Sexuality: A Practical Guide to Sexual Healing

☥

Today: Wellness Manifestations

☥

Detox Therapy: Detoxing Should Feel Good Too

☥

Akwaaba!: Dr. Akua's Ghanaian Vegan Cuisine

☥

Naturopathic Herbalist: A Course in Mastering Herbology

www.bjkbooks.com

Table of Contents

Midday Magic for Maximum Health

Transition Recipes

Introduction

My coming to eating healthy was a long road. I grew up on the typical diet of a black   family in an urban area of the United States. My mother fed us everything, all types of meat from different animals including wild game that would be brought home from my father's hunting trips which included rabbit, deer, and coons. Of course, as a child you eat what is put in front of you at the dinner table. Our neighborhood was certainly a food   desert where fresh fruits and vegetables were not readily available. I remember taking a trip to the farmers market at least once a month, which was quite a long away from our home to get fresh produce that usually only lasted about a week in our family of four.   After the fresh produce was gone, we ate out of boxes, bottles, bags and cans for the rest of the month. Our family also ate many fast food meals during the week and especially on the week-end when our parents got paid and we had a regular outing to the burger stand. It was a mom and pop burger joint that eventually closed down after McDonalds opened up in the neighborhood and we started going there for our Friday outings. We ate fried foods, preserved foods, and highly salted foods.

Shortly after reaching adulthood, many guides were put in my path to teach me the ways of the earth and the abundance that comes from eating in a more healthy way than our parents raised us on. My brother Garry came home one day after becoming a Muslim and told me the story of the worms that resided in some meats and suggested that I not eat pork, and that became the beginning of my conscious-ness to a lifestyle of healthy eating.

Over the next eighteen years, yes it has taken eighteen years to reach this point in my journey, to a knowledgeable and comfortable holistic way of eating. The steady changes included releasing all animal flesh, dairy products, fast foods, sweets, processed foods, non-organic foods and changing the way I prepare food. Through my studies I was introduced to preparing live foods through a local health food deli and eventually eating fresh foods in their electric state became the norm coupled with a vegan lifestyle balanced with both cooked and live foods.

Introduction to Food Science

Do you ever take the time to consider what keeps our bodies going on a daily basis.? We have been numbed by society to only focus on the physical appearance and that leaves us unconscious of our body's interior parts. Everything that is manifest on a physical level in our lives is first manifested on the unseen level and that includes our physical bodies. We have yet to grasp the knowledge of taking care of ourselves on the unseen level first, and the best way to do that is through our eating lifestyle. I say eating lifestyle because changing what you eat is not a diet, diets are temporary. Instead, an eating lifestyle gives you something to commit to for your health as long as you live.

The body temple houses many functions that require proper nutrition, and food is the best form of nutrition available. Each body system functions on its portion of the foods you eat, therefore, providing the body with a variety of vegetation, grains, legumes and water will maximize the overall function of the body. As I mentioned before live vegetation is electric that means the energy of the nutrients that you take in extends the life of your cells and maintains the tissues, organs and systems better than cooked foods, which are devalued of more than half the nutrients through the cooking process. Any food that is cooked above 110° looses more than half its nutrients from the excess heat destroying vitamins, minerals and enzymes.

High vibration foods includes fresh fruits, vegetables, fresh juices, smoothies and combinations of uncooked vegetation prepared by chopping, and mixing with convenient appliances like the food processor, juicer, and blender. Establishing a plant-based eating lifestyle requires dedication to changing a lot of old habits, but with commitment, knowledge, and a little motivation you can spice up you life with recipes like the ones you will find here. It is easier than you think.

You body is a divine sanctuary and it should be treated and nurtured with the respect and understanding that it is one of your most greatest assets.

Maintaining a healthy pH means being conscious of what you put in your body.

Water

The most important food for our systems is H^2O, water makes up 60% of every cell in the body. It is the primary life substance needed for you and your family to be healthy.

Your body uses water for digestion, and transporting nutrients. It dilutes your bodies waste by reducing the waste's toxicity and aids in excreting the waste from the body. Water regulates the temperature of the body through your sweat glands. It keeps your skin soft and smooth. If you don't give your body enough water, it becomes toxic and dehydrated. When the body is toxic its pH is either too acidic or overly alkaline.

The body's **potential for hydrogen (pH)** is in layman terms, how much water is in your body for the function of your cells. It is at a healthy level at 6.4. Below 6.4 is considered acid and above 6.4 is alkaline. All foods also have a pH level and it is recommended for your health to eat a balance of 20% acid and 80% alkaline foods.

When the body is acidic, disease can easily manifest. Also, a body that is overly alkaline can create an environment that stresses the internal organs. A pH imbalance is specific to the inability to use carbohydrates and fats. An imbalance can produce gland problems in the endocrine system.

Some alkaline foods:

Apple	Cauliflower
Avocado	Collards
Banana	Eggplant
Blackberry	Ginger root
Blueberry	Kale
Cantaloupe	Mustard Greens
Cherry	Garlic
Grape	Lentil
Grapefruit	Lettuce
Honeydew	Okra
Lemon	Onion
Mango	Parsley
Nectarine	Potato
Lime	Pumpkin
Orange	Sea vegetables
Papaya	Squash
Pear	Sweet Potato
Peach	Yam
Raisins	Lentils
Raspberry	Oats
Pineapple	Quinoa
Tangerine	Almonds
Watermelon	Flax seeds
Beet	Pumpkin seeds
Strawberry	Sunflower Seeds
Bell pepper	Coconut oil
Broccoli	Olive oil

Some acid foods

Cranberry	String beans
Date	Tofu
Dried fruit	White beans
Fig	Amaranth
Guava	Barley
Plum	Brown rice
Pomegranate	Buckwheat
Prune	Corn
Tomato	Millet
Carrots	Oat bran
Chard	Brazil nut
Chutney	Hazelnut
Rhubarb	Pecan
Spinach	Pine nuts
Aduki beans	Pistachio
Chickpea	Walnut
Fava beans	Spelt
Green pea	Rye
Kidney beans	Wheat
Lima beans	Pumpkin seed oil
Navy beans	Grape seed oil
Peanut	Sunflower oil
Pinto beans	Almond oil
Snow pea	Sesame oil
Soy beans	Safflower oil

All animal flesh is acid.

Nutrients: What you need to feed your body
Vitamins, minerals, enzymes, amino acids, etc...

Vitamins are components of nutrition that the body needs to function and regenerate itself. The body does not need a large amount of vitamins, however, a lack of any certain one can cause a deficiency which can then results in malfunctions in specific areas of the body's systems. Knowing what your body needs is a big step to understanding how to stay healthy. Vitamins should be taken into the body through the foods that you eat. However, because of the standard diet of overcooked, toxic filled and denatured foods that our family consumes, most eating lifestyles require a dietary supplement in the form of a multivitamin to supply the body with adequate nutrients. If you elect to take a multivitamin, make sure it is derived from a natural, plant-based source. Synthetically produced vitamins have added chemicals that alter the body's natural function and could be dangerous if taken in excessive amounts.

This section is intended to give you general information on the different vitamins and minerals.

Vitamin A - Beta Carotene is a plant-based source found in most vegetables that helps prevent infections, boosts immune function which protects against illnesses such as flu and cancers. Vitamin A forms and maintains healthy skin by preventing acne, it slows the process of aging and is needed for skin and tissue repair. Vitamin A promotes healthy hair, is essential in cell growth and development, and mucous membranes such as healing and preventing gastro-intestinal ulcers. Vitamin A aids vision in dim light or night blindness and maintains healthy eyesight. Sources of vitamin A are plentiful in the natural foods - alfalfa, apricots, asparagus, beets, broccoli, cabbage, cantaloupe, carrots, dandelion greens, garlic, grapefruit, greens (all types), kale, mango, mustard, seaweed, oranges, papaya, parsley, peppers, peaches, pumpkin, spirulina, yellow squash, tomatoes, turnip greens, watermelon and watercress.

Vitamin B1 – Thiamin is used by the body for carbohydrates conversion for energy; it breaks down fats and protein, aids in digestion, nervous system function, skin, hair, eyes, mouth, liver health and immune system function. Vitamin B1 is known to be vital in heart health, slowing age related cognitive decline like memory loss and fatigue. Sources of vitamin B1 are whole grain breads and cereals, dried beans and peas.

Vitamin B2 - Riboflavin assists with metabolism and carbohydrate conversion: it breaks down fat and protein, aids in digestion, nervous system function, is good for skin, hair, eyes, mouth, liver and assists in the formation of red blood cells. Concerns that may arise from a lack of this nutrient are anemia, cataracts, fatigue, limited free radical protection, poor thyroid function, and B6 deficiency. Sources include dark green vegetables, whole grain breads and cereals.

Vitamin B3 - Niacin enhances your energy, digestion, nervous system, skin, hair, eyes and liver. Vitamin B3 eliminates toxins, assists in the health of sex and stress hormones, improves circulation, cracking and scaling skin, digestive problems confusion, anxiety and fatigue. Sources include whole grains, bulgur, oatmeal, nuts, dried beans and peas.

Vitamin B6 - Pyroxidine is for enzyme protein metabolism, red blood cell production, formation of nerve and muscle tissue, DNA/RNA, B12 absorption, immune function and brain function. A deficiency could result in depression, sleep and skin problems, anxiety and fatigue. Food sources include dried beans, peas, nuts, whole grain breads, cereals and bananas.

Vitamin B12 – Cobalamin provides healthy nerve cells, red blood cell production and assists with iron functions. Deficiencies can result in anemia, fatigue, constipation, loss of appetite or weight, numbness and tingling in hands and feet, depression, dementia, poor memory and oral soreness. Sources include fortified vegetable and grain products.

Vitamin C - Ascorbic acid is needed for collagen, which holds the body's cells together including bones, cartilage, muscle and vascular tissue. It helps maintain capillaries, teeth, speeds up the healing of wounds and damaged bones, aids in iron absorption and helps protects other vitamins from oxidation. Vitamin C is used in cleansing toxins from the body, preventing dental cavities, inflammation of gums and skin issues. Food sources are citrus fruits, berries, melons, dark-green vegetables, tomatoes, peppers, cabbage and potatoes.

Vitamin D – Calciferol helps form and maintains bones and teeth, it is vital in calcium and phosphorus absorption, bone mineralization. If a deficiency is experienced, bone loss, osteoporosis and thyroid problems may occur. Vitamin D is made by the body when it's exposed to sunlight. A minimum of fifteen to thirty minutes of sun exposure everyday is recommended as an adequate supply to the average person. Vitamin D as a vegan food source is found in mushrooms. Other vegetarian sources include eggs and nut milks is fortified with vitamin D. Vitamin D does not occur naturally in cow's milk.

Vitamin E – Tocopherol is an antioxidant; it stabilizes cell membranes, aids immune system functions, protects against cardiovascular disease, macular degeneration and cataracts, and is good for the Integumentary System. If a deficiency is present, anemia, bruising, hot flashes, eczema, psoriasis, and muscle weakness may be experienced. Food sources include nuts, vegetable oils, wheat germ, whole grain breads and cereals and green leafy vegetables.

Vitamin K – Phylioquinone helps synthesize substances needed for blood clotting and maintenance of bone metabolism. Deficiency indicators are red spots around coiled hair follicles, bruises in the skin, hemorrhages in skin and gastrointestinal problems. Food sources include spinach, green leafy vegetables, cabbage, broccoli, cauliflower, tomatoes and whole wheat. Vitamin K is made in the body by bacteria in the intestines. Supplementation is rarely needed.

Boron is a trace mineral that assists in the prevention of bone loss. It also assists the body to maintain minerals such as calcium, magnesium and phosphorus. Studies show boron is evident in mental alertness, muscle growth, fat and sugar conversion and the body's steroid production. Boron is present in most vegetables and fruits namely apples, carrots, dark greens, grapes, nuts, pears and whole grains.

Calcium is basically needed for every function in the body. Calcium is stored in the bones and is released into the body as needed to strengthen and support the teeth, the heart, nerves, muscles and all body systems. Calcium needs other nutrients to function. Deficiencies in calcium are evident in osteoporosis, arthritis, muscle cramps, irritability, anxiety and colon cancer. Food sources include turnip greens, okra, mustard greens, kale, broccoli, oats, white beans, navy beans, black beans, chick peas, pinto beans, etc. Calcium is a major component in soil, it is present in most fruits and vegetables.

Chromium is needed in the body for energy. It is vital in glucose metabolism and the synthesis of cholesterol, fats and proteins as well. Chromium deficiency is common because it is depleted in most soils. Chromium rich foods include brown rice, corn, dried beans, mushrooms, potatoes and whole grains.

Copper, although a minute amount is needed, is used in several systems of the body. In the circulatory system, copper helps form red blood cells. In the skeletal system, it helps in the formation of bones, and it helps in joint health and collagen formation. Signs of deficiency include anemia, balding, diarrhea, fatigue, and skin problems. An excessive copper supplement intake can be fatal. Copper can be found in nuts like almonds and pecans. Fruits like oranges and raisins supply an adequate amount. Vegetation containing copper are avocados, beets, broccoli, dark leafy greens, garlic and radishes. Other sources are barley, molasses, lentils, mushrooms and soybeans.

Folic Acid helps form hemoglobin in red blood cells and aids in the formation of DNA. When a deficiency happens, anemia, diarrhea, loss of appetite, headaches, heart palpitations and forgetfulness can occur. Food sources include cereals, dark green leafy vegetables, dried beans and peas, fruits and whole grain breads.

Magnesium is responsible for about 300 biochemical reactions including muscle and nerve functions, heart rhythm, immune system proficiency, strong bones, calcium, copper, potassium, vitamin D and zinc regulation. Deficiencies include a loss of appetite, cramps, fatigue, nausea, seizures and vomiting. Foods sources include almonds, artichokes, beans, bran, nuts, oats, okra, pumpkin, quinoa, spinach and squash.

Manganese is needed for blood sugar regulation, bone growth, energy, nerves, immune system, and protein and fat metabolism. Deficiencies include eye problems, hearing problems, heart problems, high cholesterol, hypertension, irritability, memory loss and pancreas stress. Food sources include avocado, blueberries, green veggies, legumes, nuts, pineapple, seaweeds, seeds and whole grains.

Phosphorus is needed for utilizing carbohydrates, fats and protein, bone growth and a good level of energy. Deficiencies include anxiety, fatigue, pain in the bones and general body weakness. Food sources include asparagus, bran, brewer's yeast, corn, garlic, legumes, nuts, seeds (sesame, sunflower and pumpkin) and whole grain.

Potassium aids in blood pressure health, nervous system health, cellular maintenance and works with sodium to control the body's water balance. Deficiencies can manifest as constipation, edema, diarrhea, headaches, insomnia, low blood pressure, nervousness, and salt retention. Food sources are avocado, banana, brown rice, dates, figs, garlic, nuts, potatoes, raisins, spinach, winter squash, wheat bran and yams.

Selenium is an antioxidant that works with vitamin E and is necessary for immune system function, tumor prevention and thyroid health. It is also beneficial for heart and liver health. Deficiencies could cause destruction of the heart and pancreas, immune system weakness and sore muscles. Food sources include broccoli, brown rice, seaweed, garlic, oats, onions, whole wheat breads and cereals.

COQ10 is a powerful antioxidant, it stops oxidation of LDL cholesterol, assists in energy production, also known for its anti-aging properties, it is important to heart, liver and kidney health. Ailments associated with deficiencies include cardiac arrhythmias, congestive heart failure, diabetes, fatigue, gingivitis, stroke, high blood pressure, and a poor immune system. Food sources include broccoli, nuts and spinach.

Zinc supports enzymes, immune system health, wound healing, normal growth and development during pregnancy, childhood and adolescence. Growth retardation, hair loss, diarrhea, impotence, eye and skin lesions, loss of appetite, weight loss, and wounds that are not easy to heal are signs of deficiency. Food sources include beans, legumes, nuts, rice, seeds and whole grains.

In Your Health Foods Kitchen

Your kitchen should always be clean and well sanitized, using natural methods of cleaning and disinfecting such as castile detergents and soaps, lavender oil, lemon juice, vinegar, and peppermint oil. There are also many non-toxic cleaners now available in your local health foods market. This is the most important room in your house for your longevity and health. Your food is your medicine, your food is your energy, your food is your body builder and your food is your life force.

Some helpful tools and equipment that you should have in your live foods kitchen are:

Water filter system	Juicer
Blender	Food processor
Spiral slicer	Small citrus juicer
Sharp knives	Wood cutting boards
Mixing bowls various sizes	Platters various sizes
Mixing spoons	Tongs
Glass pitcher	Grater
Cheesecloth	Strainer
Rectangular glass pans	Small handy chopper
Measuring cups	Measuring spoons
Dehydrator	Veggie Wash
Various herbs/spices	

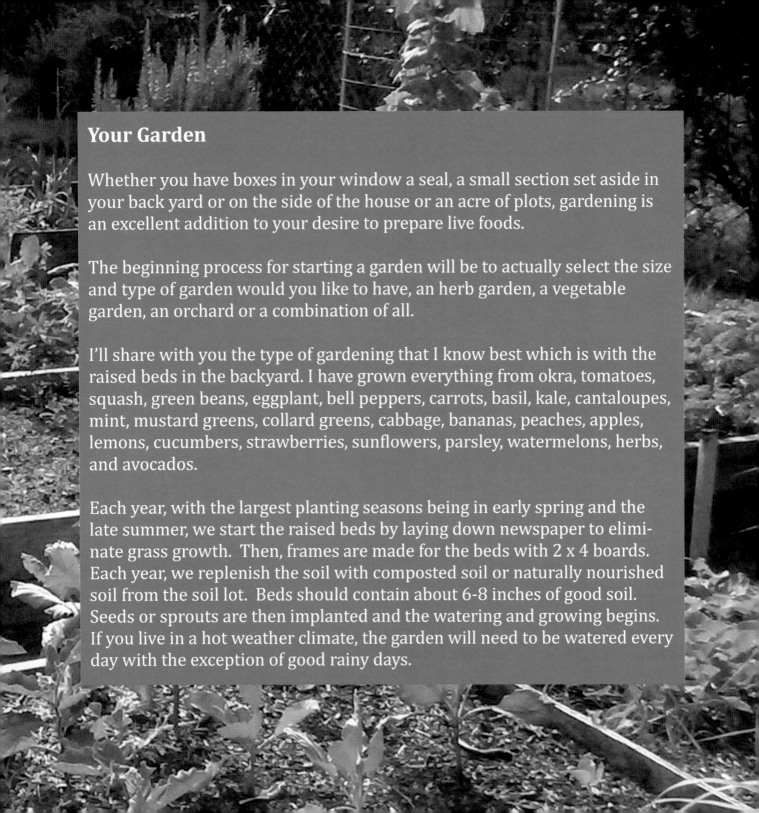

Your Garden

Whether you have boxes in your window a seal, a small section set aside in your back yard or on the side of the house or an acre of plots, gardening is an excellent addition to your desire to prepare live foods.

The beginning process for starting a garden will be to actually select the size and type of garden would you like to have, an herb garden, a vegetable garden, an orchard or a combination of all.

I'll share with you the type of gardening that I know best which is with the raised beds in the backyard. I have grown everything from okra, tomatoes, squash, green beans, eggplant, bell peppers, carrots, basil, kale, cantaloupes, mint, mustard greens, collard greens, cabbage, bananas, peaches, apples, lemons, cucumbers, strawberries, sunflowers, parsley, watermelons, herbs, and avocados.

Each year, with the largest planting seasons being in early spring and the late summer, we start the raised beds by laying down newspaper to eliminate grass growth. Then, frames are made for the beds with 2 x 4 boards. Each year, we replenish the soil with composted soil or naturally nourished soil from the soil lot. Beds should contain about 6-8 inches of good soil. Seeds or sprouts are then implanted and the watering and growing begins. If you live in a hot weather climate, the garden will need to be watered every day with the exception of good rainy days.

Learn the importance of having the ability to grow and sustain a garden for health and survival. YOU SHOULD BE ABLE TO FEED YOURSELF AND YOUR FAMILY.

Plant an herb garden of what is common to you where you are; basil, parsley, green onion, rosemary, etc.

Herb gardens are one of the easiest types of gardens to grow. Most herbs will grow naturally without much cultivation. Herbs like to grow without much structure. For example; basil grows in abundance in the summer time. Just throw the seeds in a little turned soil, pat, water, and it grows beautifully.

Teaching the Children About Food

Our children are growing up in a world that bombards them with destructive dietary habits consistently. It is our duty as parents to equip them with love, proper nourishment, a sound mind, a healthy body, a vessel filled with self-esteem and the confidence to perform their best in a system that is not designed with them in mind. Teaching them about food is going to be beneficial for them throughout their lives.

It is ideal to prepare your child healthy meals each day. A proper nutritious meal will include a grain, two vegetables, a bean, legume, nut or seed. They should also be given seasonal fruit daily. However, if they must eat outside of the home, instruct them on what to eat and what not to eat. They will listen because you have taught them and you lead by example the importance of taking care of the body by eating the correct foods.

Take your children grocery shopping with you or down to your local organic farm and show them how to select the best foods for their bodies. Include them in meal preparation time and allow them to also prepare the meals for the family according to their creativity. I guarantee some interesting meals will come about. Learn and teach your child the importance of the balance between eating live foods and cooked foods. With a family's eating habits consisting of a majority of live foods, you will cut out a lot of illnesses and dis-ease in the family's lifestyle. Whole children are happy and healthy.

Recipes for Holistic Health

Brain Power Starters

Upon waking, the body has just come out of a regeneration process where it has used many nutrients to rebuild and replenish cells, tissue and organs during your sleeping hours. It is important to give your brain a boost of energy in the morning to start your day.

During the hours of 5 and 7am, the colon is at its optimal functioning level and if the body is in order with its natural cycle you will eliminate waste during these hours. From 7to 9am, the earth cycle of the body starts and the dominate organ is the stomach. Morning nourishment is vital for the brain and body function throughout the day.

Your brain needs proteins and good fats to start itself every morning. Therefore, oats, grains, nuts, and protein rich greens are excellent for starting the day.

Adding a little fruit for flavor and your natural sugars is also a good way to raise the energy level in the morning.

Starting your morning with juicing is excellent to get some much needed nutrients assimilated for your daily activities.

Juicing is an excellent way to ease the stress on the digestive system and still get maximum nutrition; however, it is a highly concentrated form of nutrition. High concentrations of nutrients add nothing extra to the body. The body will flush out or store for a limited amount of time what it cannot use immediately. To prevent organ stress of the kidneys, juice should be diluted 1:1 with natural water. A serving of juice is measured at 8 ounces, therefore 4 ounces of juice to 4 ounces of water is recommended. The greatest benefits that juicing has on the digestive system are easy assimilation and immediate use of the chlorophyll for blood hemoglobin.

Nutritional juice includes all greens, fruits, and vegetables. It is best to limit the mixing of fruits and vegetables. The majority of the juice content should be vegetable based; fruit can be used to flavor bitters. Juice should always be made fresh and consumed immediately.

Coconut Water

One young coconut with the green hull shaved off.
Pierce a hole in the top large enough for a straw to fit through.
Insert straw and enjoy.

Nutrients: beta carotene, B complex vitamins, protein, iodine and good fat.

Body Nourishment: Coconut water is full of electrolytes for maximum hydration of the body. Nourishes the digestive system, body tissues, tapeworms, boost male sexual fluids, flushes the kidneys and it can rid the body of intestinal worms.

Carrot Beet Delight

8 -12 organic carrots
1 small to medium beet cleaned and peeled
1 organic cucumber
2 cups of spring water

Juice vegetables through the juicer, combine with water and serve. Serves 4

Nutrients: beta carotene, calcium, iron, copper, manganese, fiber, folic acid, magnesium, chlorophyll, silica, potassium, vitamins A, B complex, C, E and K. phosphorus, sodium,

Body Nourishment: Helps increase oxygen intake, builds the blood, regulates the body's pH, high in antioxidants, nourishes the eyesight, and respiratory system.

Plain Carrot Juice
Juice 5 carrots for 4 – 8oz. of juice, add an equal amount of filtered or spring water, drink and enjoy.

Plain Beet Juice
Juice 4 small or 2 large beets for 4 – 8oz. of juice and add an equal amount of filtered or spring water.

Broccoli Juice

Juice 4 cups of broccoli to produce 4 – 6 oz. of juice and add 1 cup of filtered or spring water and drink immediately.

Nutrients: beta-carotene, folic acid, boron, calcium, chromium, iron, magnesium, phosphorus, protein, potassium, selenium, sulphur, vitamins A, B2, B6, C, E and K.

Body Nourishment: Broccoli has anti-cancer properties and helps to boost the immune system. Broccoli also helps prevent constipation, lowers high blood pressure, eyesight, stimulates weight loss and protects against toxemia.

Cabbage Juice

Juice 4 cups of cabbage for 2 – 4 oz. of juice and add an equal amount of filtered or spring water and drink immediately.

Apple Juice

Juice 2 apples of your choice (Gala, Red, McIntosh, Green, Granny Smith, Jazz, etc.) to produce about 4 – 8oz of juice. Add 4 –8 of filtered or spring water .

Nutrients: beta-carotene, calcium, phosphorus, potassium, vitamin B and C.

Body Nourishment: Apples are anti-bacterial, anti- inflammatory, antiviral, acts as an astringent, diuretic, stabilizes blood sugar and assists in good digestion and weight loss. Other areas of nourishment include colon health by reducing inflammation, diarrhea and constipation. Eating apples help to clean your teeth and promote healthy gums. For the internal organs, apple benefits the arteries, liver, gallbladder, lungs, lymphatic system and help ease the symptoms and heal gout, asthma, morning sickness and removes radiation and toxins from the body.

Cucumber Juice

Juice 2 cucumbers for 4 – 6 oz. of juice and drink immediately for maximum nutritional use.

Nutrients :beta carotene, calcium, chlorophyll, fiber, folic acid, magnesium, phosphorus, potassium, silica and vitamins A, C and E.

Body Nourishment: Cucumber strengthens the connective tissue in muscles, tendons, ligaments, cartilage and bone. It reduces swelling under the eyes and helps with sunburn. Cucumber is good for the skin.

Celery Juice

Juice 3 stalks of celery for 4– 6 oz. of juice; add an equal amount of spring or filtered water and drink immediately.

Papaya Juice

Peel and slice ½ - 1 papaya into pieces. In a blender combine with 1—2cups of water, depending on desires thickness. Drink immediately for maximum nutritional use.

Nutrients: beta carotene, calcium, magnesium, potassium, protease, vitamins C and E.

Body Nourishment: Papaya is good for the digestive system, the lungs, menstrual irregularities and colon health. Papaya can also help reduce the risk of stroke and heart attack. It also enhances hair growth, healthy nails and skin.

Mango Juice

Peel and slice 2 ripe mangos off the seed and place into a blender, add 2 –3 cups of water depending on the desired thickness and blend well. Strain if needed. Drink and enjoy.

Nutrients: amino acids, beta carotene, calcium, iron, magnesium, niacin, pectin, potassium, vitamins C and E.

Body Nourishment: Mango works as an antiseptic, diuretic, and as a laxative. Mango is also used to increase iron in the body, reduce fever, relieve indigestion, kidney inflammation, respiratory ailments, lower blood pressure and aid a weak digestive system.

Pineapple Juice

Juice ½ pineapple for 4-6 oz. of juice, add an equal amount of filtered or spring water and drink immediately. You can also use the blend and strain method if you don't have a juicer.

Nutrients: beta carotene, carbohydrates, fiber, magnesium, manganese, potassium, vitamins B complex and C.

Body Nourishment: Pineapples are rich in digestive enzymes, is anti-inflammatory, anti-bacteria, anti-viral, diuretic, blood enhancer, strengthens bones, protects against and reduces edema, constipation, expels intestinal worms and prevents sore throat.

Kale Strawberry Juice

2 cups of filtered or spring water
10 strawberries fresh
5 leaves of kale

Juice kale and strawberries through the juicer and combine with water stir and serve. Serves 1

Nutrients: beta carotene, calcium, iron, copper, manganese, folic acid, iodine, vitamins B1, B2, B6, C, E and K.

Body Nourishment: Nourishes the respiratory system, protects against arthritis, asthma, cancer, heart disease and inflammation.

Cool Green Drink

5 leaves of kale
1 cup of spinach
1 cucumber
2 cups of spring water

**Juice vegetables through the juicer, combine with water and serve.
Serves 2**

Nutrients: beta carotene, calcium, iron, copper, manganese, folic acid, magnesium, chlorophyll, silica, potassium, vitamins A, B1, B2, B6, C, E and K.

Body Nourishment: Regulates the body's pH, high in antioxidants, nourishes the eyesight, respiratory system and the connective tissue, builds muscles, ligaments, tendons, cartilage and bone, skin, swelling and burns.

Goddess Healing Potion

1 oz. of wild blue green algae juice
2 oz. ginger juice fresh
5 oz. natural water
1 tsp. agave nectar

Stir in a 12oz. glass and enjoy the rich tantalizing burst of energy!
Serves 1
Nutrients:B-12, B complex, chlorophyll, protein, iron, beta-carotene, calcium, Vitamin C and A, folic acid, biotin, niacin

Body Nourishment: Alleviates congestion, aids in digestion, use for vitamin and mineral deficiencies, heavy metal poisoning, purifies the blood, stops inflammation, rejuvenates cells, obesity, yeast over growth, enhances memory, and supports the glands.

Almond Milk

1 cup raw almonds (soaked)
4 cups spring water
1 tsp. cinnamon
1 dash vanilla extract

In a blender, combine all ingredients and blend well. You may choose to strain or not.
Serves 4

Nutrients: protein, calcium, iron, zinc, magnesium, potassium and vitamin E.

Body Nourishment: Excellent brain and bone food to get you started for the day. Almonds are good for the lungs, liver, nervous system, improves energy and sexual vitality.

Power Boost Almond

½ cup of almonds (soaked overnight)
1 organic banana (frozen for thicker smoothie)
¼ cup of organic oats
3 cups organic almond milk
1 tbsp. flaxseed oil
1 tbsp. organic agave nectar or agave to taste

Combine all ingredients and blend well. Pour and enjoy.
This is an excellent source of morning protein.
Serves 2 - 4

Nutrients: folic acid, glucose, fructose, calcium, iron, zinc, magnesium, potassium, protein, omega-3, omega-6 fatty acids, vitamins A, B, B6, C and E.

Body Nourishment: This smoothie is excellent food for your brain, digestive system, muscles and bones. It improves stamina and works to increase your energy level. It nourishes the lungs, nervous system and liver. It increases sexual vitality and contains a large amount of protein.

Creamy Almond Peach Bliss

2 cup of almond milk
2 organic bananas (frozen for thicker smoothie)
¼ cup of almond butter
1 cup peaches (fresh or frozen)
agave to taste

**Combine all ingredients and blend well.
Pour and enjoy.**

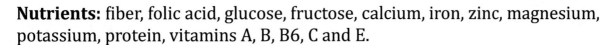

Nutrients: fiber, folic acid, glucose, fructose, calcium, iron, zinc, magnesium, potassium, protein, vitamins A, B, B6, C and E.

Body Nourishment: This smoothie is excellent food for your brain, digestive system, muscles and bones.
It improves stamina and works to increase your energy level. It nourishes the lungs, nervous system and liver. It increases sexual vitality and contains a large amount of protein.

Mango Munch

1 large organic mango (sliced off seed)
1 cup of pineapple (cubed)
¼ cup of organic oats
2 cups rice milk
1 tbsp. flaxseed meal
1 tbsp. organic agave nectar

**Combine all ingredients and blend well.
Pour and enjoy.   Serves 2 - 4**

Avocado Heaven

½ small avocado
1 organic banana
1 cup pineapple (cubed)
½ cup mango slices
2 cups rice milk

Add preferred sweetener if needed. Combine all ingredients and blend well. Pour and enjoy.
Serves 2

Nutrients: beta-carotene, calcium, iron, potassium, magnesium, manganese, fiber, niacin, pectin, lysine,

Body Nourishment: Nourishes and aids the circulatory system and protects against blood clots, aids in relieving ailments of the respiratory. Excellent for sleep disorders including insomnia. Balances the liver and relieves hemorrhoids.

Blackberry Smoothie

1 cup strawberries fresh or frozen
1 cup blackberries fresh or frozen
2 cups water or your favorite nut milk
1 banana
2 tbsp. of agave
1 tbsp. of powdered greens of your choice

Blend until smooth.
Serves 2

Nutrients: iodine, protein, glucose, fructose, sucrose, iron, zinc, potassium, chlorophyll, vitamins B1, C and K

Body Nourishment: Nourishes the digestive system, protects against high blood pressure, heart disease, inflammation, and cancer.

Blueberry Smoothie

1 banana
1½ cup fresh blueberries
2 tbsp. agave nectar sweetener
2 cups almond milk

Blend ingredients until smooth.
Serves 2

Nutrients: protein, iron, zinc, calcium, potassium, magnesium, biotin and fiber sodium, pectin, glucose, fructose, sucrose, vitamins B2, B6, C and E.

Body Nourishment: Improves vision, heart function, balances body fluids, improves blood pressure, reduces risk of stroke and lowers LDL, Nourishes the digestive system and urinary tract. Protects the brain against oxidative stress, macular degeneration, protects against cataracts and glaucoma, varicose veins, hemorrhoids and peptic ulcers, relieves diarrhea, constipation and normalizes bowel function

Strawberry Cashew Delight

½ cup strawberries fresh or frozen
2 cups of your favorite nut milk
2 bananas
2 tbsp. of cashew butter
2 tbsp. of agave or agave to taste.

Blend all ingredients until smooth and serve.
Serves 2

Nutrients: iodine, protein, glucose, fructose, sucrose, iron, zinc, potassium, chlorophyll, vitamins B1, C and K

Body Nourishment: Nourishes the digestive system, protects against high blood pressure, heart disease, inflammation, and cancer.

Mean Green Smoothie

1 cup spinach
½ cup of organic oats
½ mango
½ cup of strawberries
1 banana
2 tbsp. agave nectar
2 tbsp. of a Green formula of your choice
3 cups of filtered or spring water

Combine all in the blender and mix well.
Serves 4

Nutrients: calcium, protein, copper, phosphorus, selenium, magnesium, iron, zinc, potassium, manganese, boron, dietary fiber, vitamins B1, B2, B6 and C.

Body Nourishment: Protects against heart disease, diabetes, lowers cholesterol, acts as a stool softener, anti-cancer and balances the body's pH.

Oats and Apple Granola Bars

1 gala apple organic (cored and chopped)
½ cup organic quick oats
¼ cup almond, soaked overnight/at least 2 hours
6 medium dates (pitted)
½ tsp. cinnamon
½ cup raisins
½ cup coconut, shredded (optional)

Lightly chop the almonds and dates in a food processor. Add the chopped apples and spices and pulse until it is a chunky granola texture. Stir in the remaining ingredients and shape into bars. Dehydrate for 5 hours or until firm.
Serves 6

Nutrients: calcium, iron, copper, phosphorus, selenium, magnesium, zinc, potassium,
manganese, boron, dietary fiber, protein, vitamins B1, B2, B6 and C.

Body Nourishment: Protects against heart disease, diabetes, lowers cholesterol, stool
softener, anti-cancer and balances the body's pH.

Strawberry Almond Swirl

2 bananas
½ cup almonds (soaked)
1 cup strawberries
4 tbsp. agave nectar
2 tbsp. coconut oil

Combine almonds, bananas, half of the strawberries, 2 tbsp. of the agave nectar and the coconut oil in the food processor until you have a creamy pudding. (*add a little almond milk if too thick*)

In the blender, add the remaining strawberries and agave nectar and blend to a red sauce, after pudding is put in the bowls for serving, drop a spoon full of strawberry sauce in and swirl for presentation and an extra wow of flavor.
Serves 2

Nutrients: protein, calcium, iron, magnesium, zinc, potassium, vitamin B6, C and E.

Body Nourishment: Improves energy, increase sex hormone production, aids the   digestive system, assist in reversing alcoholism, purifies blood, acts as a liver tonic, protects against anemia, constipation, high blood pressure, jaundice

Blueberry Bars

1 cup raw almonds (soaked)
½ cup shredded coconut
6 medjool dates
1 cup fresh blueberries
Agave to taste

In a food processor combine almonds and dates until processed well. In a bowl add agave, coconut shreds and blueberries. Stir ingredients together then shape your blueberry mix into bars and dehydrate for 3 - 5 hrs.
Serves 4 - 6

Nutrients: beta-carotene, calcium, iron, copper, magnesium, iron, zinc, potassium, boron, dietary fiber, vitamins B1, B2, B6, C and E.

Body Nourishment: Protects against stomach ulcers, bronchitis and anemia. Helps   regenerate the pancreas, lowers cholesterol and is a powerful antioxidant. Excellent brain and bone food and is good for the lungs, liver, nervous system and sexual vitality.

Sweet Oats Pancakes

2 bananas
½ cup oats blended to a meal
¼ tsp. cinnamon
4 medjool dates (soaked)

Peel and mash bananas in a bowl, pour in blended oats, blend dates as close to a liquid as possible and add to other ingredients in bowl and sprinkle in cinnamon. Mix well with a mixing spoon.

When mixed well, scoop with serving spoon a generous amount onto plate and shape as a pancake. Allow to stand for about 15 minutes to naturally crust over or place in dehydrator for 45 minutes to 1 hour if desired.   Serves 2 - 4

Nutrients: protein, calcium, fructose, potassium, pectin, folic acid, copper, magnesium, iron, boron, fiber, B-complex and vitamin C.

Body Nourishment: Works as a spleen, blood and energy tonic. Stimulates the colon, prevents sore throats, coughs and bronchitis. Increases energy, assists in reversing drug addictions, depression and paralysis.

Midday Magic
for Maximum Health

Your digestive system jump starts the body's functions bright and early at 5am every morning and works continuously until around 3pm when it begins to wind down to allow other body systems to do their jobs at full capacity like assimilating the nutrients and preparing for the cleansing and regenerative process as you sleep at night. It is helpful when you are concerned about your health and longevity to have a little knowledge about the best way to consume foods that provide maximum nutrition. I call this next section of recipes Midday Magic because the ingredients for these recipes are packed with vitamins, minerals and the fiber needed to normalize the digestive system for optimum functioning. Eat these meals with consistency and watch your health flourish and change for the better.

The recipes are super easy to prepare and don't require you to buy the whole market to make one meal. In fact, most recipes have less than ten ingredients and require less than thirty minutes of preparation time. The variety of the dishes can be mixed and mingled to where you never have to have the same meal twice. However, a few of my favorite combinations include:

The Best Veggie Sandwich in the World with Garden Kale Salad

Veggie Pizza with Cheezy Kale

Zahra's Sunny Raw Nori Rolls with Goddess Supreme Nourishment

Veggie Fettu with a side of Akua's Favorite Asparagus and Curry Cabbage

Couscous Dressing with Green Beans on the Side and Hot Greens

The Best Veggie Sandwich In the World

2 slices sprouted bread
½ organic cucumber
1 organic tomato
2 whole leaves of organic green leaf or romaine lettuce
1 avocado, alfalfa sprouts
¼ tsp. garlic powder
¼ juice of a lemon

Slice cucumber long and thin. Slice tomato sandwich style. Dress your bread if desired. Lay on the lettuce, tomato, cucumber, alfalfa sprouts. Remove avocado from shell, mash and mix in a bowl with garlic powder, lemon juice and desired seasonings. Top alfalfa sprouts with avocado mix, close sandwich, cut in half and enjoy. Increase ingredients based on number of people to serve.

Nutrients: beta-carotene, folic acid, calcium, iron, potassium, sulfur, silicon, chlorophyll, histamine, lycopene, fluorine, copper, lecithin, vitamins B, B6, B-complex C, E and K.

Body Nourishment: Nourishes the respiratory system, helps with indigestion, weight gain, relieves constipation, kills tapeworms, assists in reversing diabetes and high blood pressure, balances liver function and soothes the bladder, anti-bacterial and anti-viral properties, reverses erectile dysfunction, has anti-aging properties, boosts your enzymes with alfalfa sprouts.

Vegan Pizza

1 zucchini
½ yellow bell pepper
¼ red onion
½ bunch of broccoli
A handful of Black olives (sliced)
1 cup cherry tomatoes

Dice all vegetables and set aside

Marinara Sauce
2 or 3 medium tomatoes, cut in quads
1 cup sun dried tomatoes (soaked or in olive oil)
3 cloves garlic
1 tbsp. lemon juice
½ - 1 tsp. sea salt
2 tbsp. Italian seasoning mix
¼ cup fresh basil
3 tbsp. agave nectar
3 tbsp. extra virgin olive oil

Combine all ingredients in a blender until smooth.

Spread marinara evenly and thick over organic whole wheat pizza crust, sprouted pita bread or dehydrated flax crust. Then drop on veggies evenly around the pizza and top with cashew cheese. Slice as desired.
Serves 6

Cashew Cheese
2 cups raw cashews (soaked)
½ cup spring water
1 tsp. sea salt
2 tbsp. lemon juice
1 tsp. mustard powder
3 tbsp. nutritional yeast

Combine all ingredients in the food processor and process for 2 - 3 minutes until thick and creamy.

Nutrients: sulfur, beta-carotene, folic acid, calcium, protein, copper, phosphorus, magnesium, iron, zinc, potassium, dietary fiber, vitamins B1, B2, B6, C and E.

Body Nourishment: Protects against heart disease, stroke, kidney stress, bladder disorders, obesity, ulcers and cataracts. Good for muscle building and as an anti-inflammatory and diuretic.

Basil Spring Rolls

1 cup cabbage
½ cup purple cabbage
2 avocados
2 tbsp. Namashoyu
1 tbsp. garlic powder
1 tbsp. fresh basil
½ fresh squeezed lemon juice
6 collard green leaves or green leaf lettuce

Cut collard leaves off stems to produce two wraps per leaf. Chop all other veggies and in a mixing bowl. Spread mix on collard leaves and roll.
Serves 6

Nutrients: beta-carotene, protein, folic acid, calcium, iron, potassium, sulfur, chlorophyll, fluorine, iodine, copper, lecithin, omega-3, omega-6 fatty acids, vitamins B1, B6, B-complex C, E, K and U.

Body Nourishment: Works as an antibiotic and has anti-viral properties. Nourishes the lungs, liver and stomach. Prevents obesity, skin disorders, and dental problems. Cabbage is excellent for eye infections, radiation exposure, tuberculosis, yeast infections and gout.   Avocado nourishes the blood, balances liver function, and is super for the digestive system.

Carrot Tuna Sandwich

12 - 20 organic carrots (depending on the size)
¼ cup red bell peppers (diced)
¼ cup celery (diced)
2 nori sheets cut into flakes
3 tbsp. vegan mayonnaise
2 tbsp. liquid aminos
Green leaf lettuce
Steak tomatoes
Alfalfa sprouts

Juice carrots and put carrot pulp in a mixing bowl. Put in all other ingredients and mix well, spread on sprouted bread with veggies and serve. Serves 4 - 6

Nutrients: beta-carotene, folic acid, calcium, potassium, magnesium, silica, sodium, fiber, chlorophyll, protein and vitamins C.

Body Nourishment: Nourishes the blood, detoxifies the liver. Protects against cancer, acne, diabetes, hypertension and insomnia.

Waluna

4 cups walnuts soaked over night
¼ cup water (add more if needed)
½ small white onion diced
2 stalks of celery
2 Tbsp. organic kelp granules
½ cup sweet relish *(or relish to taste)*
3 Tbsp. of vegan mayonnaise *(optional)*
1 Tsp. sea salt

Grind walnuts and celery in the food
processor adding a little spring water at a time to achieve pate
consistency. When pate consistency is reached, transfer to mixing bowl
and add all other ingredients and mix well. Add more salt or relish to suit
your waluna taste! *I like it with water crackers topped with romaine
lettuce.*

Nutrients: protein, iodine, beta-carotene, calcium, chlorophyll, iron, fiber,
phosphorus, potassium, B complex , vitamins, B6 and C.

Body Nourishment: Nourishes the brain, large intestines, the blood and whole
body system.

Zahra's Sunny Raw Nori Rolls

2 cups hulled sunflower seeds (soaked)
4 green onions (green parts)
¼ cup fresh parsley
½ lemon juice
¼ cup of water
2 tbsp. liquid aminos
4 cloves garlic (2 tsp.)
8 sheets of nori
1 carrot (peeled and sliced into thin strips)
1 cucumber (peeled and sliced into thin strips)
1 avocado thinly (sliced)
1 cup sprouts of your choice

In a food processor add sunflower seeds, green onions, parsley, lemon juice, liquid aminos, garlic, water and mix until creamy. Set aside.

On cutting board, lay out 1 nori sheet, spread 2 serving spoons of sunflower pate on nori sheet. Stack carrot strip, cucumber strip, avocado slice and sprouts in narrow line 1 inch from long edge of nori sheet. Fold nori sheet over vegetables and roll sheet away from you as tightly as possible. Dab edge of nori sheet with water to seal and close. Repeat with remaining ingredients. Cut each roll into 6 bite-size pieces with serrated knife.
Serves 6

Nutrients: protein, beta-carotene, zinc, copper, lecithin, folic acid, calcium, iron, chlorophyll, phosphorus, potassium, selenium, sulfur, omega-3, omega-6 fatty acids, B complex, vitamin C and E.

Body Nourishment: Works as an antioxidant in the body and has antibiotic properties. Nourishes the digestive system in bowel function and cleanses the lymph system.

Summer Green Rolls

10 green leaf lettuce leaves
1 cup of green peas (organic frozen)
2 avocados (diced)
1 stalk of celery thin sliced coins
½ lemon (juiced)
2 Tbsp. of sesame oil
2 tsp. liquid aminos

Rinse whole lettuce leaves and set to the side for drying. Soak peas until thawed. Slice celery stalk into very thin coins. Dice avocado and cover with lemon juice. In a mixing bowl, combine celery, peas, sesame oil and lightly stir to coat with oil. Drop in avocado and liquid aminos and again lightly stir as to not mash the avocado.

Dip a table spoon full or two into each lettuce leaf, wrap, place on presentation tray and serve. Serves 5

Nutrients: beta-carotene, folic acid calcium, chlorophyll, iodine, iron, phosphorus, protein, magnesium, zinc, potassium, manganese boron, dietary fiber Omega-3 and Omega-6 fatty acids, vitamins B1, B6, C, E and K.

Body Nourishment: Helps to reduce swollen joints and good for the digestive, glandular, and excretory systems. Protects against high cholesterol, ulcers and obesity.

Veggiladas

8 organic green leaf lettuce leaves for wraps
2 ears of corn
¼ cup of chopped cilantro
1 tomato (diced)
1 large avocado (diced)
1 tsp. chili powder
½ cup chopped red peppers
1 tsp. Vegit Seasoning

Set lettuce aside for wrapping.

In a large bowl, mix all ingredients well making sure some of the avocado cubes get smashed.

Put a small amount of mixture into each lettuce leaf. Add your favorite salsa or pico de gallo to taste and wrap.
Serves 8

Nutrients: beta-carotene, folic acid, calcium, iron, potassium, silicon, chlorophyll, fluorine, copper, lecithin, phosphorus, protein, omega-3, omega-6 fatty acids, zinc, vitamins B1, B6, B-complex C, E and K.

Body Nourishment: Nourishes the digestive system, cardiovascular system, nervous system and reproductive system. Helps with insomnia, stress and sexual addictions. Builds blood, bones and muscles. Prevents constipation, lubricates lungs and protects against ulcers.

Avocado Tacos

2 large ripe avocados
1 stalk of broccoli
1 tbsp. of fresh cilantro
1 large ripe salad tomato
½ lemon
1 tbsp. garlic powder
1 tbsp. liquid aminos
1 tbsp. chili powder
12 whole leaves of green leaf lettuce

Set lettuce a side, this is your taco shell. Slice broccoli off of stalk into very small pieces. Open, pit and scoop out avocado into mixing bowl over broccoli. Chop up cilantro very fine and add to bowl. Dice tomatoes and add to bowl with all the listed seasonings and mix just enough for seasoning to blend in, yet avocado chunks still remain visible. When mixture is to your taste, scoop small spoons full in a
lettuce leaf, wrap it up and enjoy. You may also add a topping of your favorite raw or homemade salsa.
Serves 6

Nutrients: beta-carotene, fiber, folic acid, calcium, iron, potassium, sulfur, chlorophyll, chromium, selenium, fluorine, copper, lecithin, phosphorus, protein, omega-3, omega-6 fatty acids, vitamins B2, B-complex C, E and K.

Body Nourishment: Nourishes the blood, prevents constipation, lubricates lungs, balances the liver, recommended for erectile dysfunction, insomnia, and ulcers. Protects against stroke, heart disease and cataracts.

Veggie Fettu

3 Zucchini, peeled

With a vegetable peeler create long fettuccini style strands into the bowl. Rotate the zucchini and repeat slicing, stop at the seeds.

Marinara Sauce
2 tomatoes cut in quads
2 tbsp. agave nectar
¼ tsp. sea salt
½ tbsp. Italian herb seasoning
½ cup basil (fresh)
1 cup sun-dried tomato in olive oil or soaked
½ jalapeno pepper
2 medium garlic cloves

Blend ingredients until smooth but thick. Top zucchini with marinara sauce.
Serves 4

Nutrients: beta-carotene, folic acid, dietary fiber, manganese, selenium, phosphorus, niacin calcium, iron, potassium, sulfur, germanium, copper, protein, vitamins B6, C and K.

Body Nourishment: Good for hydration, respiration, headaches, kidney ailments and poor circulation. Acts as an antibacterial, de-wormer. Has anti-cancer properties by protecting against radiation and free radicals. Relieves constipation, high blood pressure, anti-bacterial and anti-viral.

Pecan Nori-Nut Rolls

2 cups raw pecan (soaked)
¼ cup of water (add more if needed)
1 tbsp. pressed garlic
1 tbsp. oregano
1 tbsp. cumin (powdered)
1 tbsp. of grape seed oil
1 tsp. sea salt
1 tsp. cayenne pepper
2 cups shredded romaine lettuce
1 sliced avocados
1 cup alfalfa sprouts
6 sheets Nori Seaweed

In a food processor, add pecans and seasonings and mix until smooth.
Spread the pate in the Nori sheet, add lettuce, sprouts and avocado.
Wrap the seaweed sheet tightly and seal with water. Cut into bite sized
coins and serve.
Serves 6-12

Nutrients: beta-carotene, folic acid, calcium, iron, potassium, sulfur,
chlorophyll, protein, omega-3, omega-6 fatty acids, vitamins A, B, C, E and K.

Body Nourishment: Nourishes the liver, lungs, prevents constipation, skin
disorders and ulcers.

Cheezy Kale Salad

1 bunch of organic kale greens
½ cup Sundried tomatoes (diced)
1 tsp. garlic powder
1 tbsp. extra virgin olive oil (marinade massage)
1 tbsp. liquid aminos
2 tbsp. Nutritional Yeast (more to taste)

Wash kale greens and tear the leaf from the stalk into very small pieces by hand. Place greens in a large mixing bowl along with the olive oil, lemon juice, garlic, seasoning and mix well. Add all other vegetables and mix.
Serves 6

Nutrients: beta-carotene, calcium, chlorophyll, iron, phosphorus, potassium, protein, sulfur, fiber, omega-3, omega-6 fatty acids, B complex vitamins, B6, B12 and C.

Body Nourishment: Nourishes the respiratory, digestive, circulatory and immune systems. Protects against heart disease,

Gar-DEN Kale Salad

1 bunch of organic kale greens
¼ cup red bell pepper (chopped)
1 tbsp. pressed garlic
1 carrot (shredded)
2 tbsp. extra virgin olive oil
1 tbsp. liquid aminos
½ lemon (juiced)
2 avocados (pitted and cubed)

Wash kale greens and tear the leaf from the stalk into very small pieces by hand. Place greens in a large mixing bowl along with the olive oil, lemon juice, garlic, seasoning and mix well. Add all other vegetables and mix. Serves 6

Nutrients: beta-carotene, calcium, chlorophyll, iron, phosphorus, potassium, sulfur, fiber, pectin, omega-3, omega-6 fatty acids, B complex vitamins, B6 and C.

Body Nourishment: Nourishes the respiratory, digestive, circulatory and immune systems. Protects against heart disease, Avocado is known as one of the super foods because it has a wonderful supply of most nutrients including good fats.

Gar-LIC Kale Salad

1 bunch of organic kale greens
¼ cup tahini
1 tbsp. pressed garlic
1 tbsp. sesame seeds
1 tbsp. liquid aminos or to taste
½ lemon (juiced)

Wash kale greens and tear the leaf from the stalk into very small pieces by hand. Place greens in a large mixing bowl along with the tahini, lemon juice, garlic, seasoning and mix well.
Serves 6

Nutrients: beta-carotene, calcium, chlorophyll, iron, phosphorus, potassium, protein, sulfur, fiber, B complex vitamins, B6 and C.

Body Nourishment: Nourishes the respiratory, digestive, circulatory and immune systems. Protects against heart disease.

Hot Greens

1 bunch of organic kale greens
8 sundried tomatoes in olive oil or soaked
½ habanera pepper
½ tbsp. olive oil
1 tbsp. liquid aminos (or to taste)

Place all ingredients in a food processor, blend well and serve.
Serves 4

Nutrients: beta-carotene, folic acid, calcium, iron, potassium, sulfur, chlorophyll, protein, vitamins A, B, C, E and K.

Body Nourishment: Nourishes the liver, lungs, prevents constipation, skin disorders and ulcers. Kale assists with weight loss, joint problems and dental problems.

Curry Cabbage

1 green cabbage (shredded)
1 red pepper (wedged)
½ yellow pepper (diced)
2 medium carrots (coined)
2 cloves garlic (pressed)
1 medium tomato (wedged)
1 tsp. liquid aminos
½ cup olive oil
½ tbsp. curry powder

In a large mixing bowl, combine all ingredients and toss well to marinade curry and oil over all ingredients.
Serves 4 - 6

Nutrients: beta-carotene, folic acid, calcium, iron, potassium, sulfur, chlorophyll, protein, vitamins A, B, C, E and K.

Body Nourishment: Nourishes the liver, lungs, prevents constipation, skin disorders and ulcers.

Kerubo's Plantain Slaw

2 cups chopped green cabbage
¼ cup chopped carrots
¼ cup chopped broccoli
1 ½ cup plantain chopped in small quads
1 tbsp. agave nectar
2 tbsp. vegan mayonnaise

In the food processor pulse the cabbage, carrots, and broccoli into coleslaw consistency. In a mixing bowl add all ingredients and toss well, chill and serve.
Serves 6

Nutrients: beta-carotene, folic acid, calcium, iron, potassium, sulfur, chlorophyll, protein, vitamins A, B, C, E and K.

Body Nourishment: Nourishes the liver, lungs, prevents constipation, skin disorders and ulcers.

Warm Spinach Salad

1 lb. of organic baby spinach
1 organic avocado
1 organic tomato
2 tbsp. of organic virgin olive oil
1 tbsp. of raw oats
1 tbsp. of liquid aminos

Mix all ingredients in a large bowl. Mix with your loving hands well and serve.
Serves 6

Nutrients: beta-carotene, folic acid, calcium, iron, potassium, sulfur, chlorophyll, fluorine, copper, lecithin, phosphorus, protein, oleic acids, amino acids, omega-3, omega-6 fatty acids, vitamins A, B6, B-complex C, E and K.

Body Nourishment: Nourishes the blood, prevents constipation, lubricates lungs, balances the liver, recommended for erectile dysfunction, insomnia and ulcers. Protects against stroke, heart disease and cataracts.

Mixed Greens Delight

½ Napa cabbage
½ green leaf lettuce
¼ green cabbage
1 cup parsley leaves

Chop greens in long thin slices and layer greens in a salad bowl.

Green Delight Dressing

2 garlic cloves
4 green onion stalks
½ jalapeno pepper
1 small bunch cilantro
1 lime (juiced)
½ cup of water
½ tsp. sea salt (or to taste)
2 tsp. olive oil
½ tsp. cumin powder

Top greens with dressing on each individual plate.
Serves 6

Nutrients: beta-carotene, folic acid, calcium, iron, sulfur, iodine, protein, selenium, magnesium, iron, potassium, vitamins B1, B6, C, K and U.

Body Nourishment: Protects against breast cancer, heart disease, strokes, cataracts and diabetes.

OMG Walnut Pate

1 lb. of walnuts soaked overnight
2 stalks of celery (diced)
1 large carrots
¼ yellow onion
2 cloves of garlic
1 tsp. flaxseed oil
½ cup of fresh parsley
1 tbsp. of sage
1 tsp. of thyme and rosemary ground
1 tsp. of poultry seasoning (Sea Salt if needed)
1 avocado
Add a small amount of water by the tablespoon if needed.

In a food processor, chop walnuts, and flaxseed oil to a paste consistency. Place in a separate bowl. In a food processor, lightly chop celery, carrots, onion and add to bowl. Add chopped garlic, ground sage, thyme, rosemary, chopped parsley and poultry seasoning. Mash in avocado and mix everything together by hand. Mold nicely unto a platter and garnish.
Serves 8

Nutrients: protein, beta carotene, calcium, iron, phosphorus, potassium, protein sodium, pectin, selenium, sulfur, histamine, omega-3, omega-6 fatty acids, B complex vitamins, C and E.

Body Nourishment: Nourishes the immune, respiratory and digestive system. Protects against inflammation, balances liver function and soothes the bladder.

Wakame Wonder

1 cup of organic dehydrated wakame
1 cup of organic petite green peas
1 lemon (juiced)
1 tbsp. garlic red pepper paste
Liquid aminosto taste

Soak wakame for 1 hour. When all leaves are fluffy, strain off the remaining water combine all ingredients, mix well and serve.
Serves 6

Nutrients: beta-carotene, fiber, folic acid, calcium, iron, potassium, sulfur, chlorophyll, chromium, selenium, fluorine, copper, lecithin, phosphorus, protein, omega-3, omega-6 fatty acids, vitamins B2, B-complex C, E and K.

Body Nourishment: Nourishes the blood, prevents constipation, lubricates lungs, balances the liver, insomnia, and ulcers. Excellent digestive system aid.

Akua's Favorite Asparagus

1 bunch of asparagus
½ juiced orange
½ orange thinly (sliced)
1 tbsp. agave nectar
1 tbsp. olive oil
1 tbsp. liquid aminos

Lay asparagus on a platter. Pour on orange juice. Drizzle on oil. Drizzle on agave. Drizzle on liquid aminos. Top with orange slices and serve. Serves 6

Nutrients: beta-carotene, iodine, zinc, folic acid, calcium, iron, potassium, vitamins B, B1, C and E.

Body Nourishment: Nourishes the circulatory system. Cools fevers, inhibits tumor growth, works on kidney health and eliminates darkness under the eyes.

Plantain Salad

2 ripe plantains
1 stalk of green onion (chopped)
1 tbsp. liquid aminos
1 tbsp. curry powder

Peel and slice very ripe plantains. Cut into thick coins. Chop green onions. Mix all ingredients, let chill for 30 minutes and serve.
Serves 6

Nutrients: beta-carotene, folic acid, calcium, iron, potassium, sulfur, chlorophyll, selenium, protein, vitamins B, B6 and C.

Body Nourishment: Nourishes the Integumentary system and the digestive system. Improves energy, stamina, sleep and mood. Also used to relieve constipation, depression, exhaustion, hypertension, ulcers and hemorrhoids. The recipe has anti-viral and anti-infection properties.

Okra and Tomato

½ lb. of fresh okra
2 tomatoes (diced)
2 fresh garlic cloves
¼ purple onion (sliced in thin strips)
2 tbsp. liquid aminos
1 tsp. basil flakes

Slice okra into small coins, dice garlic and dice tomatoes. Combine all ingredients in a bowl and mix well. Add liquid aminos or sea salt if desired.
Serves 6

Nutrients: beta-carotene, calcium, iron, phosphorus, potassium, sodium, sulfur, lycopen, histamine, B complex, vitamins, C and E.

Body Nourishment: Nourishes the respiratory system. Protects against heart disease, cataracts and preserve the body's balance of fluids.

Green Beans on the Side

3 cups of green beans or asparagus beans
2 tbsp. of liquid aminos
½ cup of sliced almonds

Soak green beans overnight. Combine all ingredients in a bowl and mix well.
Serves 6

Nutrients: beta-carotene, protein, calcium, iron, phosphorus, magnesium, potassium, sodium, pectin, zinc, antioxidants, B complex and vitamin C.

Body Nourishment: Nourishes the brain, bones, liver, respiratory system and nervous system.

Couscous Dressing

1 cup of couscous
1 shredded carrots
¼ cup of finely diced red peppers
¼ cup of finely chopped parsley
1 tbsp. olive oil
1 tbsp. poultry seasoning
1 tbsp. ground sage
Liquid aminos to taste

Cover the couscous with spring water, set aside and let it soak up all the water until light and fluffy; about 20 minutes. When all the water is absorbed, add all the remaining ingredients, mix well and serve.
Serves 4 - 6

Nutrients: beta-carotene, potassium, thiamine, chlorophyll, magnesium, calcium, zinc, folic acid, iron, dietary fiber, omega-9 fatty acid, vitamins A, B Complex, B6, C, E and K.

Body Nourishment: Works as an antioxidant and protects against cancer in the bladder, cervix, colon, larynx, esophagus and lungs. Good for the eyes, nerves, diabetes and prevents perspiration, asthma and arthritis.

Goddess Supreme Nourishment

4 leaves of romaine lettuce or organic spring mix
1 handful of alfalfa sprouts
10 cherry tomatoes cut is halves
¼ cup red bell pepper sliced thin and long
½ cup of okra sliced in coins

Cover the whole plate with the alfalfa sprouts by pulling them loose. Thinly slice the romaine lettuce and as the next layer on the plate. Slice the okra as the next layer and top with the red bells and tomatoes. Set aside while you prepare the goddess dressing.

Goddess Dressing

2 tbsp. Olive oil
1 tbsp. liquid aminos
1 tbsp. agave nectar
2 shakes of cayenne pepper
Add other herbs and spices to suit your tastes.

Mix all ingredients well in a cup. Pour over salad and enjoy.

Nutrients: beta-carotene, calcium, chlorophyll, iron, phosphorus, potassium, protein, sulfur, fiber, pectin, omega-3, omega-6 fatty acids, B complex vitamins, B6 and C.

Body Nourishment: Nourishes the respiratory, digestive, circulatory and immune systems. Protects against heart, disease bowel disorders and womb ailments. Olive oil is good fat.

A Bunch of Greens

1 bunch of collards
1 bunch of kale
2 tbsp. flaxseed oil
1½ tbsp. agave
2 fresh garlic cloves (pressed)
1 tsp. ground cumin

Cut washed greens from around the ribs down the center. Stack leaves and roll tightly, cut into thin coins and place in bowl. Combine remaining ingredients in a separate bowl and mix well into a dressing. When ready to serve, toss dressing with greens and serve.
Serves 6

Nutrients: beta-carotene, calcium, chlorophyll, iron, phosphorus, potassium, sulfur, fiber, pectin, omega-3, omega-6 fatty acids, B complex vitamins, B6 and C.

Body Nourishment: Nourishes the respiratory, digestive, circulatory and immune systems, Protects against heart disease. Flaxseed has a wonderful supply of good fats.

Flax Seed Crackers

1 cup brown flax seeds
Spring water
Liquid aminos to taste for seasoning

Pour flaxseeds into a wide bowl and pour enough spring water on them to slightly rise above the seed level and stir in seasoning. Allow mixture to sit about 20 minutes to absorb the water. It will turn slightly slimy similar to okra. Spread cracker mix on the bottom dehydrator tray or whichever tray you have that is not gridded. Dehydrate for 8 hours or until crackers come out hard and crispy.
Serves 6

Nutrients: protein, omega-3 and omega-6 fatty acids, vitamins A, B and E.

Body Nourishment: Protects against heart disease, and nourishes the Integumentary, digestive and immune systems.

Salad Dressings

Salad dressings are truly a test of your creativity and by choice I never make the same one twice! There are few basics in salad dressings that will give you a unique tasty creation every time.

1. A good blender.
2. Your preferred oil base.
3. Water for consistency.
4. Seasonings for flavor.
5. Veggie of choice for substance.
6. Avocado or cashews for creaminess.

And a lemon twist (optional).

Enjoy creating your own salad dressings and you never have to buy salad dressings again.

It Tastes Like Ranch Dressing

½ cup cashews (soaked)
½ cup spring water
1 tbsp. lemon juice
¼ tsp. garlic (pressed)
¼ tsp. onion powder
Sea salt to taste
1 tbsp. fresh basil
½ tbsp. fresh dill weed

Blend cashews, water, lemon, garlic and onion until smooth and creamy. Add basil and dill weed and pulse briefly just to chop and mix.

Zahra's Spinach Tahini Dressing

½ cup tahini
1 handful of spinach
3 tbsp. of tamari
2 cups of water
1 cup of raisins

Blend all ingredients till smooth and creamy
Serves 4

Ginger Garlic Dressing

2 cloves garlic (chopped)
1 tbsp. fresh ginger (chopped)
2 tbsp. namashoyu or liquid aminos
2 tsp. sesame oil
3 tsp. tahini
2 tbsp. olive oil

Blend, chill and serve.
Serves 4

Divine Desserts and Drinks

Everyone loves a little sweet and delicious sometimes and what would a vegan recipe book without some indulgences in dessert! Forget what you know about all goodies needing eggs, milk, cream and baking powder, and open yourself to a world of Veggie Delights Divine Desserts! Chocolate Pudding never tasted better with a secret ingredient that gives it that smoothness that will make your finger the last thing you taste getting every bit out of the bowl. Have you even heard of Chocolate Covered Strawberry Pie? If not, these dessert recipes will open up a new way to experience sweet and healthy in your life.

Chocolate Pudding

2 medium/large avocados
½ cup of water
¼ cup of cacao powder or more
(depends on the size of the avocados)
¼ cup of agave nectar (add more if needed)
1 tsp. of vanilla extract

Combine all ingredients in a food processor and puree until smooth, adding a little more water if needed. More water will give you a thinner pudding.
Serves 4

Nutrients: beta-carotene, fiber, folic acid, calcium, iron, potassium, sulfur, chlorophyll, chromium, selenium, fluorine, copper, lecithin, phosphorus, protein, omega-3, omega-6 fatty acids, vitamins B2, B-complex C, E and K.

Body Nourishment: Nourishes the blood, prevents constipation, helps lungs, balances the liver, recommended for erectile dysfunction, insomnia, and ulcers. Protects against stroke, heart disease and cataracts.

Chocolate Covered Strawberry Pie

1 lb. fresh strawberries

Prepare the chocolate pudding recipe on page 95. Wash and take of the tops of 1 pound of fresh strawberries. Slice strawberries into very thin slices and begin to layer a glass pie dish. Leave a few strawberries whole for decorations. Once sliced strawberries are in place, pour pudding into pie dish and chill for an hour before serving.
Serves 6

Nutrients: beta carotene, calcium, iron, copper, manganese, folic acid, iodine, vitamins B1, B2, B6, C, E and K, potassium, sulfur, chlorophyll, chromium, selenium, fluorine, copper, lecithin, phosphorus, protein, omega-3, omega-6 fatty acids, B-complex.

Body Nourishment: Nourishes the respiratory system, circulatory system, protects against arthritis, cancer, heart disease, prevents constipation, inflammation, balances the liver, recommended for erectile dysfunction, insomnia, and ulcers.

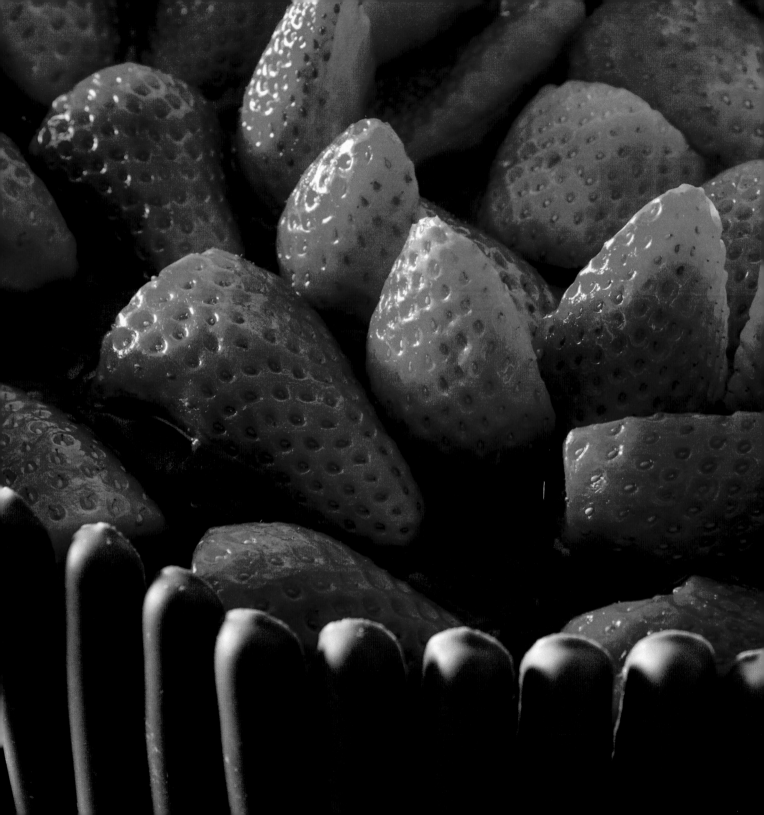

Chocolate Ball Surprise

2 cups walnut soaked at least two hours
1/3 cup organic cacao powder
8 medjool dates
1 tsp. vanilla extract

Combine walnuts, dates, cacao and process on high until well combined. The food processor should roll mixture into a ball. Gather up remaining mixture from processor bowl and shape onto the ball. Slice like a cake and serve with cute little decorations. Serves 10

Nutrients: protein, calcium, potassium, zinc, boron, copper, magnesium, fiber and vitamins E.

Body Nourishment: Nourishes the brain, large intestines and the blood. This dessert is good for the whole body system.

Fruit Salad for Akua

2 gala apples
2 bananas
2 oranges
½ pineapple
1 cup of grapes
1 juiced lemon

Slice all fruit except lemon in bite sized pieces. Mix well. Pour on lemon juice. Mix well. Chill and serve. Serves 6

Nutrients: Rich in antioxidants, beta carotene, calcium, fiber, folic acid, iron, magnesium, manganese, phosphorus, potassium, vitamins B complex, B1, B6 and C.

Body Nourishment: Nourishes the respiratory, digestive and immune systems. These ingredients act as a great detox formula for the body.

Raw Coconut Balls

1 cup raw pecan
1 cup chopped dates
¾ cup dried shredded coconut
2 tbsp. of raw agave

Grind the nuts and dates together, combine into a bowl. Add the ½ the coconut. Add just enough agave so that when you are forming the balls, they retain their shape. When balls are shaped, roll around in the remaining coconut to coat and serve. Mix will make 15-25 balls. *Options*: Balls can be served plain or for variety roll a few in cacao powder, cinnamon , or shredded coconut.

Nutrients: protein, beta-carotene, calcium, copper, fiber, magnesium, iron, potassium, B complex and B6.

Body Nourishment: Nourishes the liver, lungs, prevents constipation, skin disorders and ulcers.

Banana Mango Mix With Raspberry Syrup

5 ripe organic bananas (coined)
2 mangos (cubed)
½ cup raspberries
2 tbsp. of agave

In a mixing bowl, toss bananas and mango together. Chill in fridge for 30 minute to an hour. In a blender, combine raspberries and agave to a nice even consistency. Place chilled fruit mix in chilled glass dish and top with raspberry syrup and serve.
Serves 6

Nutrients: beta carotene, Vitamins B6, C, E, calcium, iron, magnesium, potassium

Body Nourishment: Nourishes the digestive, muscular, circulatory, excretory and respiratory systems. The recipe is an excellent for the kidneys and the liver.

Banana Mango Pie

2 cup raw walnuts (soaked 4-6 hrs)
1 cup medjool dates
8 ripe bananas (sliced)
5 strawberries
2 mangoes
4 tbsp. of agave
½ cup of coconut oil

Chop walnuts and dates in the food processor for 3 minutes. Remove from processor bowl and shape into pie crust dish. Combine mango, agave and coconut oil in the blender and blend to a puree. Begin to layer the banana slices in the pie crust and pour the mango syrup over the sliced bananas and place in the refrigerator for 3 hours to set. Garnish the top of the pie with strawberry fans.

Nutrients: beta-carotene, calcium, iron, potassium, magnesium, vitamins B6, C and E.

Body Nourishment: Nourishes the digestive, muscular, circulatory, excretory and respiratory systems. The recipe is an excellent tonic for the kidneys and the liver.

Binta's Pineapple Protein Pops

1 cup flax meal
1 cup almond pulp
½ cup pineapple pulp
½ cup agave or to taste

Mix all ingredients in a mixing bowl into to cookie dough batter consistency. Shape small wafer size round thins on baking pan and dehydrate in oven at lowest temperature until crisp. Make your favorite dipping syrup to accent your wonderful healthy snacks.

Nutrients: beta carotene, carbohydrates, fiber, magnesium, manganese, potassium, vitamins B complex, C and E, protein, calcium, iron, and zinc.

Body Nourishment: Pineapples are rich in digestive enzymes, is anti-inflammatory, anti-bacteria, anti-viral, diuretic, blood enhancer, strengthens bones, protects against and reduces edema, constipation, expels intestinal worms and prevents sore throat. Almonds are good for the lungs, liver, nervous system, improves energy and sexual vitality.

Pineapple Cheesecake with Coconut Mango Sauce

3 cups of cashews soaked
1 cup almonds soaked
30 dates soaked
1½ cup soft young coconut meat
1 lemon juiced
1 tbsp. agave nectar
1 mango neatly sliced from seed
Spring water
1 cup of fresh pineapple cubed

Mix almonds and 20 dates in the food processor until well mixed consistency should be thick. Place in glass pie dish and press evenly to cover entire dish including the sides. Mix cashews, remaining dates, ½ cup of coconut meat, lemon juice and ½ cup of fresh pineapples in food processor and mix well, adding water bit by bit to desired consistency. Pour batter unto crust and shape.

Decorate top of cheesecake with mango slices and garnish. In a blender mix remaining coconut meat, ½ of sliced mango and agave nectar to a sauce. Put in nice serving dish and chill. Serve in thin pie slices with sauce topping.

Ginger Lemonade

5 lemons
1 ginger root
¼ cup agave nectar or agave to taste
1 qt. water

Juice lemons and ginger root in a regular juicer. Add juice to water along with agave nectar sweetener to suit your taste and serve.

Nutrients: potassium, folic acid, fructose and sucrose, vitamins B6 and C.

Body Nourishment: Dissolves gallstones, protects against cancer, eases gastrointestinal stress, acts as an anti-inflammatory, prevents motion sickness, nausea and vomiting.

Mojito Mami's

5 limes
12 fresh mint leaves (rolled to release flavor)
¼ tsp. cinnamon powered
1 cup agave nectar
1 ½ qt. spring or filtered water

Juice limes with a citrus juicer. Roll mint leaves along cutting board. In a glass pitcher or punch bowl, add juice to water along with agave nectar and cinnamon to suit your taste and serve.

Nutrients: potassium, folic acid, fructose and sucrose, vitamins B6 and C.

Body Nourishment: Dissolves gallstones, protects against cancer, acts as an anti-inflammatory eases gastrointestinal stress, prevents motion sickness, nausea and vomiting.

Transition Recipes

Transitioning to a vegan eating lifestyle will take time, and working your way up to consuming eighty percent or more of your foods in their natural uncooked state may take even longer, and that's ok. In the mean time I want you to enjoy the journey with these easy vegan transition recipes for all meals. These are some of my favorite recipes that I served my family when we were making healthy eating lifestyle changes. These traditional dishes vegan style will help you to realize how unnecessary unhealthy additives can be eliminated from your meal, you won't miss the meat, butters, creams, jellies and preservatives. Take your time, love yourself in the process and remain consistent until you reach your goals.

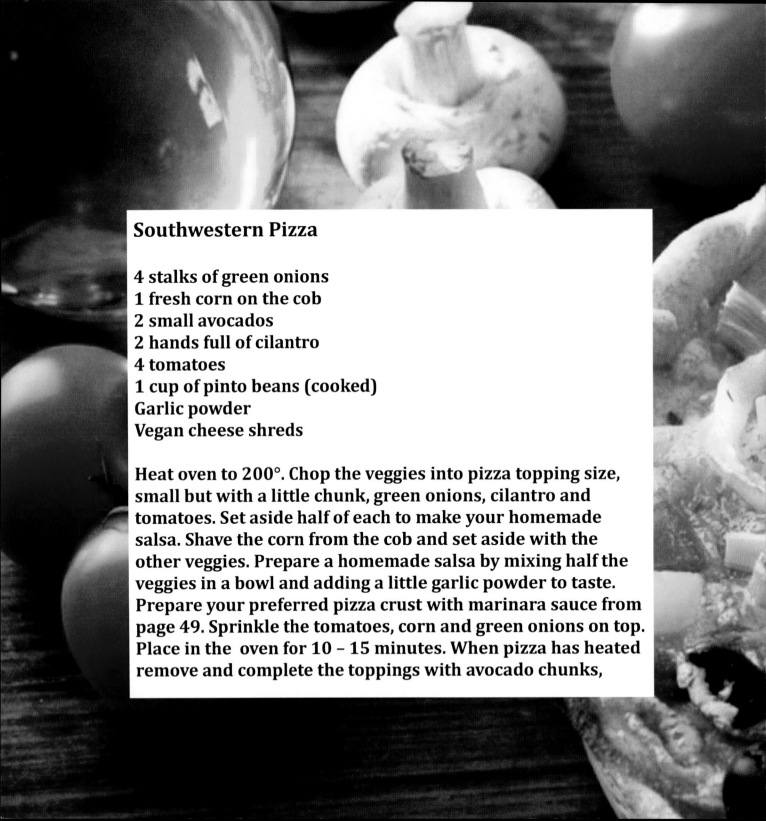

Southwestern Pizza

4 stalks of green onions
1 fresh corn on the cob
2 small avocados
2 hands full of cilantro
4 tomatoes
1 cup of pinto beans (cooked)
Garlic powder
Vegan cheese shreds

Heat oven to 200°. Chop the veggies into pizza topping size,
small but with a little chunk, green onions, cilantro and
tomatoes. Set aside half of each to make your homemade
salsa. Shave the corn from the cob and set aside with the
other veggies. Prepare a homemade salsa by mixing half the
veggies in a bowl and adding a little garlic powder to taste.
Prepare your preferred pizza crust with marinara sauce from
page 49. Sprinkle the tomatoes, corn and green onions on top.
Place in the oven for 10 – 15 minutes. When pizza has heated
remove and complete the toppings with avocado chunks,

Veggie Deluxe Pizza

½ red bell pepper
½ yellow bell pepper
½ green bell pepper
½ red onion
½ yellow onion
2 stalks of green onion
3 cloves of garlic
1 cup broccoli
¼ cup of fresh parley

Heat oven to 200°. Prepare pizza crust of choice, a vegan variety, with marinara sauce from page 49 and set aside. Chop green onions and slice all other vegetables into very thin long slices. Sautee lightly with a little olive oil and top waiting pizza crust. Heat in oven for 10 – 15 minutes or until crust is warmed. Slice and serve.
Serves 5

Tofu Scramble

1 pack of extra firm tofu
1 red bell pepper
1 green bell pepper
½ yellow onion
1 tbsp. of turmeric (powdered)
1 tomato
Liquid aminos to taste

Stir fry diced bell peppers and onion. Add tofu by hand crumbling into the skillet and add turmeric. When well mixed to an egg yellow color, remove from heat and add liquid aminos. Slice tomato and garnish in a circle around the edges of the tofu scramble.
Serves 4

Red Curry Stir Fry

1 pack of extra firm tofu (cubed)
2 cups of brown rice (cooked)
2 shredded carrots
½ onion (sliced)
2 cups of broccoli (chopped)
1 cup red bell peppers (diced)
Tamari to taste start with a few tbsp.
Organic red curry paste
Organic red pepper paste

In a wok or pan or with a small amount olive oil stir fry the cubed tofu to toughen the outside. Add veggies and stir fry together for two to three minutes. Once vegetables are cooked to your desired consistency, add rice and continue to stir. Add Tamari, red curry and pepper to taste.
Serves 6

Jama Jama

1 lb. of fresh spinach (baby or regular)
1 yellow onion (diced)
Liquid aminos to taste

Stir fry onion in a frying pan. When onions are soft and
browned, add spinach and liquid aminos. Stir over fire for 2
minutes and reduce heat. Continue warming to desired
consistency. Remove from heat and serve.
Serves 4

Mediterranean Lentils

1 lb. lentils (soaked overnight)
1 yellow onion (diced)
2 carrots (coined)
2 stalks of celery (sliced)
2 tbsp. curry powder
2 tbsp. turmeric
2 tbsp. cumin
Liquid aminos to taste

Prepare lentils by boiling 1 – 2 hours. When lentils are soft and edible, add vegetables and cook about 5 additional minutes. Remove from heat and add seasonings to taste. Serve warm as a soup or over couscous or rice.
Serves 6

Southern Split Pea Soup

1 lb. split pea
2 carrots (shredded)
1 yellow onion (diced)
½ tsp. cayenne
liquid aminos to taste

Boil split pea until done. Remove from heat and add shredded carrots, onions and seasoning. Cover for 30 minutes to allow the steam pressure to soften vegetables and cool.
Serves 6

Veggie Quinoa

2 cups of quinoa
1 carrot (grated)
½ cup red bell (diced)
½ cup green onion (diced)
2 tbsp. curry powder
2 tbsp. cumin

Bring to a boil, quinoa grains and spring water. Reduce heat to a simmer and cook for 10 - 20 minutes. Stir in vegetables and seasonings and continue to cook an additional 10 minutes or until quinoa is soft and edible. Add sea salt or liquid aminos to taste.

Plantain

2 ripe plantains
Choose plantains that have a lot of black on the skin and is soft to the touch.

2 cups of vegetable oil or red palm oil for pan frying

Heat vegetable oil in a frying pan. Peel and slice plantain in diagonals. Place slices in oil and fry to a light brown color and flip each slice of plantain over and continue the browning. Remove from pan to drain oil, cool and serve as an appetizer or side dish. Serves 4

Acknowledgements

Give thanks to the creator whose energy supplies my life. To the spirit of the ancestors whose guiding presence and earthly teachings have supplied me with love, knowledge and the will to be the spirit that I am today.

To my husband G. Chenu Gray, my sons Kazembe, Jaja, Bomani, Granny Ella Gray, who have supported me in every idea and endeavor that has ever been given to me to pursue, I say THANK YOU! And thank you my readers for allowing me to share this peace knowledge so that the circle of love and healing continues.

-Dr. Akua

About the Author

Dr. Akua, naturopath, spiritualist and master teacher, is the Operations Director for A Life of Peace Education Wellness Institute, an international holistic health education and wellness non-profit organization. She is the author of numerous books including, The Natural Health and Wellness Manual, Naturopathic Reiki Volumes I, II and III, Detox Therapy, Naturopathic Herbology, Veggie Delights: Recipes for Holistic Health, Eating Live for Maximum Nutrition and Wellness, Akwaaba! : Dr. Akua's Ghanaian Vegan Cuisine, Today: Wellness Manifestations and Holistic Sexuality: The Practical Guide to Sexual Healing.

Dr. Akua has shared the gifts of her works with the international communities of the USA, Canada, The Caribbean, Israel, The Philippines, England, Qatar, Germany, Japan and Ghana. An outstanding educator for 20+ years, Dr. Akua holds degrees and certifications in Naturopathy, Education, Telecommunications, Metaphysics, Hypnotherapy, Iridology, Reiki, Pranic Healing, Shiatsu, Colon Hydrotherapy, Midwifery and African Nutritional Science. At A Life Of Peace Wellness Education Institute Dr. Akua currently teaches classes in Naturopathy, Sacred Goddess Temple Rites of Passage, Nutrition, Holistic Health Business, Vegan Foods Preparation, Naturopathic Reiki, Holistic Doula Training, and many areas of alternative health options.

Dedicated to issues of Pan African empowerment and health - Dr. Akua has worked on family empowerment and healing as a Spiritual Counselor, Holistic Health Consultant and Holistic Birth Coach. She continues to enhance her spirit through many avenues of consciousness elevation. Akua currently lives bi-continental between Texas and Ghana. The nurturer of three SUNS who are the mirror of the life she has lived. She shares these accomplishments with her divine reflection of 32 years Dr. Chenu.

Dr. Akua is available for Live Foods Classes and Retreats.

Made in the USA
Coppell, TX
20 February 2022

73855226R00090